One Cold, Wet Night

Story by Joy Cowley and June Melser
Illustrations by Deirdre Gardiner

One cold, wet night,
the farmer got out of bed

2

and went outside.   Then…

the horse
jumped into the bed and said,
"I'm going to be warm tonight."

4

The cow
jumped into the bed and said,
"I'm going to be warm tonight."

5

The sheep
jumped into the bed and said,
"I'm going to be warm tonight."

6

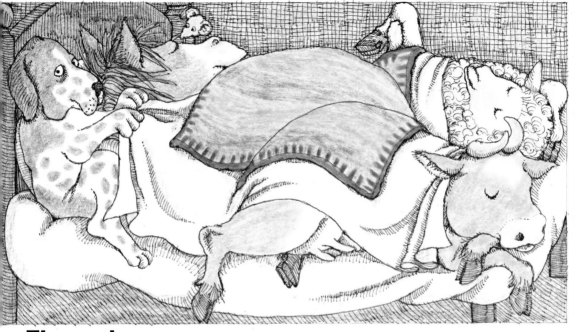

The dog
jumped into the bed and said,
"I'm going to be warm tonight."

A giant weta
jumped into the bed.

8

The farmer came back.

"Get out of my bed!"
he yelled.

The horse ran out.
Skiddle-dee-doo.

The cow ran out.
Skiddle-dee-doo.

The sheep ran out.
Skiddle-dee-doo.

The dog ran out.
Skiddle-dee-doo.

14

But the giant weta
stayed in the bed.

And the farmer said,
"I'll sleep on the couch tonight."